FRED BASSET

by ALEX GRAHAM

Chapmans Publishers
A Division of the Orion Publishing Group Ltd
Orion House
5 Upper St Martin's Lane
London WC2H 9EA

First published by Chapmans 1993

© Associated Newspapers Ltd 1993

ISBN 1–85592–668–7

Printed and bound in Great Britain by
The Guernsey Press Co. Ltd, Guernsey, Channel Islands.

Oops! Tripped over my ears!

I suppose some people might think that was funny!

A disagreement! He would rather play the piano than watch television

...And I'm the one in the middle...

It's not fair! Me left at home here

© Associated Newspapers Ltd, 1993

9155

IF YOU HAD KEPT YOUR HEAD DOWN YOU WOULDN'T HAVE SLICED INTO THE BUNKER!

AND IF YOU HADN'T MISSED THAT SHORT PUTT ON THE EIGHTEENTH WE WOULDN'T HAVE LOST!

And them out enjoying themselves on the golf course

ALEX GRAHAM

Just look at the mud I'm dragging in! Disgraceful!

© Associated Newspapers Ltd, 1993

9156

Have they no pride in their home?

And then to let me sit on the furniture

ALEX GRAHAM

I might have caught that cat if I hadn't been tied to this tree!

9159

THE LIGHTS HAVE CHANGED! GET A MOVE ON IN FRONT!

9160

WHY DON'T YOU LOOK WHERE YOU'RE GOING, YOU FOOL?

LOOK AT THAT IDIOT TURNING RIGHT WITHOUT SIGNALLING!

Really, motoring is no pleasure nowadays